What Is Soft?

by Miriam Sklar

ISBN: 978-1-338-75088-1
Illustrated by John Lund

Published by Scholastic Inc., 557 Broadway, New York, NY 10012

10 9 8 7 6 5 4 68 25 26 27/0

Printed in Jiaxing, China. First printing, January 2021.

My towel is soft.

My hair is soft.

My robe is soft.

My bear is soft.

My bed is soft.

My pillow is soft.

Zzzzzzz!